FRANZ SCHUBERT

QUARTET

for 2 Violins, Viola and Violoncello
E♭ major / Es-Dur / Mi♭ majeur
D 87

Ernst Eulenburg Ltd

London · Mainz · Madrid · New York · Paris · Tokyo · Toronto · Zürich

Quartet

I

Franz Schubert, Op. 125 № 1
1797-1828

    E. E. 1220   Ernst Eulenburg Ltd

8

10

II

Scherzo. Prestissimo

12

Trio

40

50

Scherzo da Capo al 𝄐

E. E. 1220

III

Adagio

14

70

80

pizz.

arco

Allegro

24